Contents

Introduction

This book is intended for a particular group of children. It is aimed specifically at those children who are having difficulty with their number work. Commonly, the children will not yet have achieved the competencies in Number normally expected in a seven year old child. These are children who require an individual education plan under the new arrangements for children with special educational needs. The book outlines the skills, the teaching strategies, the activities and the follow-up work appropriate in this context.

How to use this book

There are two ways in which this book can be used in the classroom.

1 It can be used as the basis of an individual education plan. There may be several children in your class who require the provision of these plans, which can be constructed using the outline of topics and the structure of skills provided in this book. The best method here is to adopt a four-stage approach:
- identify and list the precise skills you feel the child needs to acquire
- use the Numeracy Support Book to help you construct an order of work, giving a progression from one skill to the next
- select the teaching strategies and tactics in each topic that most appropriately match the specific needs of the child
- identify and prepare the activities and follow-up work.

2 The book can be also used as a resource to help you provide focused support for particular number skills. Some children may be having difficulty with a certain skill, e.g. subtraction, and need specific attention. This book supplies teaching strategies and tactics to help you assist the children's acquisition of these skills, and the activities necessary for rehearsal and reinforcement. In this sense, it is possible to 'dip into' the book, using it as a resource when necessary, either on a 'one-off' basis or to help a small group of children.

Structure and content

The book is divided into sections under numerical skills headings. In each section, you will find:

1 Teaching strategies

The teaching strategies provide a step-by-step progression of strategies for helping children to understand and assimilate a particular piece of mathematics. They are outlined briefly in a clear and logical progression that is easy for the teacher to scan and absorb. These teaching strategies inform the nature of the assistance given to the children as they attempt the activities and the follow-up work.

2 Tactics

The tactics offer a range of different practical techniques for helping children to learn. A teacher may well select those from the list that he or she finds most appropriate. Factors that will influence the choice of tactics will include the resources available in the classroom, the nature of the difficulties experienced by that particular child, and the particular preferences of the teacher.

3 Activities

The activities are quick and easy to prepare, and straightforward to teach. Most of the activities use materials provided in the Resource Pack (e.g. number cards), so that the teacher does not have to spend time making extra materials. The children can record their efforts easily where appropriate. Each activity can be done by one child working alone, or by two or three children working together. The activities are arranged in an approximate order of difficulty.

4 Follow-up work (photocopy masters)

The follow-up work provides carefully graded examples of the specific numerical skills. The steps between one example and the next have been made as small as possible, and there is a high level of repetition. It is suggested that the children are encouraged to use the tactics outlined in each section to complete the sheets.

Further information

The Numeracy Support Book provides a detailed breakdown of the progression and structure of skill acquisition in each topic. Taking each numerical topic in turn, the book constructs a skill-hierarchy, outlining the steps that the child must accomplish in order to acquire that skill. Alongside this structure are the precise tactics that will assist the child with each step.

The analysis of each numerical skill can be extremely useful information for any teacher involved in planning a detailed programme of study, either for an individual, for a group, or for the whole class.

① Adding to 20

Strategies

Step 1 Start with counting, leading to counting on. Rehearse counting to twenty, and beyond.

Step 2 Read addition as counting on, first counting on 1 and 2, and then 3. Read 12 + 2 as *twelve count on two...*

Step 3 Develop the counting on strategy to include counting on 4 and 5. Read 7 + 5 as *seven count on five...*

Step 4 **Memorise** the doubles: 2 + 2, 3 + 3, 4 + 4 and so on. Rehearse these in written and oral form.

Step 5 Use a mixture of doubles knowledge and counting on, e.g. read 6 + 9 as *six add six is twelve, and three more, thirteen, fourteen, fifteen.*

Tactics

Number line

The number line is the most vital image. Ask each child to make a number line using cut-out numbers, which they can Blu-Tack onto the table in front of them. They should refer to this for all calculations. It is essential that they internalise the image of a line of numbers, 1 to 20.

For example, 11 + 3 =, they point to the first number – *eleven* – then count on, moving their fingers along one for each number spoken: *twelve, thirteen, fourteen.*

Start by counting on just 1, then increase to 2 and 3. Provide plenty of practice: 13 + 1, 15 + 1, 6 + 1, etc.

Fingers

Children can move on from counting along the number line to using their fingers to help them count on in their heads. So, to perform an addition such as 13 + 3, the child points to the 13 on the number line, and then holds up fingers to match the number to be added – *thirteen add three* – looking from the 13 on the number line to their three standing fingers. They count on from 13, folding down one finger for each number spoken (this helps them keep track of how many have been added).

The trick here is to use the fingers to represent the number to be added, and then fold them down one at a time as you count on.

Chanting the doubles

It is important that the children memorise the doubles facts. They need to chant the doubles – *three and three is six, four and four is eight,* and so on. They can use fingers, for example, holding up three fingers on each hand making six fingers in all.

For six and six, seven and seven etc., use cubes to demonstrate, but then focus on the memorising skills. Use written and oral repetition.

Encourage the children to make up a rhyme or rap to help them memorise, e.g. *Six and six is twelve, down and down we delve. Seven and seven is fourteen, looking up, see where we've been ...*

Activities

Note: All the activities can be undertaken either by individuals or by small groups. The activities are given in increasing order of difficulty.

ACTIVITY **1**

Number cards (1 to 20), number track (1 to 21), lots of different coloured cubes
Shuffle the cards and place them face down in a pile. The children turn over the top card, e.g. 16 and place it face up on the table. They place a coloured cube on it, e.g. red, and count on one. They place a cube of the same colour on that number on the track, i.e. a red cube on 17. They continue until every number on the track has a cube on it except one. Repeat this activity for counting on two or three – using a track up to 22 or 23.

ACTIVITY **2**

Number track (1 to 20), a counter, a dice
The children place a counter on 1, and write '1 +'. They throw the dice, e.g. 4, and complete the second part of the addition, i.e. '1 + 4 ='. They move the counter on to match the dice, and then complete the addition, 1 + 4 = 5.
The next addition starts where the counter now is (i.e. 5 +). The children throw the dice and continue as before.

ACTIVITY **3**

Dominoes
Spread out all the dominoes face up. The children find all the dominoes which are doubles, e.g. 6 and 6, 5 and 5. They draw round each one and write the total number of spots inside each outline. They can then choose some other dominoes and do the same, e.g. 6 and 5, 4 and 3.

ACTIVITY **4**

A book with about 25 pages (numbered), cubes
The children open the book at random and write the page number, e.g. 17. They guess what the page number will be three pages on and write it down. They count on three pages (remembering that each side of each page is numbered) to check. If correct they can take a cube. They continue until they have at least six cubes.

ACTIVITY **5**

Number cards (1 to 20)
Split the cards into two sets (1 to 9) and (10 to 20), shuffle them separately and place them face down in two piles. The children turn over the top card of each pile, e.g. 12 and 4, and place them side by side. They add the two numbers and write the addition: 12 + 4 = 16. They check the addition on a number line.
They continue until all the cards are turned over.

ACTIVITY **6**

Dominoes
Spread out all the dominoes face up. The children select two (e.g. 6, 5 and 2, 5) and find the total number of spots (i.e. 18), using their knowledge of doubles to help them. What is the highest score they can make using two dominoes? What is the lowest?

Photocopy masters
Numeracy Support Book
pages 24 to 27

Associated units
Abacus 4 N1 Addition

2 3-digit numbers

Strategies

Step 1 Rehearse counting to 100. Emphasise the repetitive elements of the count: *thirty-**one**, thirty-**two**, thirty-**three**, ...* followed by *forty-**one**, forty-**two**, forty-**three**, ...* Provide written and oral practice of counting.

Step 2 Use a selection of 3-digit numbers (none with a 0 in the tens place) and 'read' these by covering the first number (i.e. the hundreds digit) and reading the remaining 2-digit number, then uncovering the hundreds and reading the whole number.

Step 3 Extend the counting aspect of numbers beyond 100. Use a number line and order numbers along it. Deal with numbers beginning 'one hundred' first.

Step 4 Count in tens above 100. Continue over 200, then over 300, etc.

Step 5 Order any five or six numbers. Adopt this procedure: *Look at the hundreds digit only – which is largest? Now look at the tens digit – which is largest? Now look at the units...*

Tactics

Place-value cards

These cards enable children to build up numbers, starting with 2-digit numbers with which they feel confident. They can make 37 using cards 30 and 7. Once they are confident making any 2-digit number, they can add a hundreds card, e.g. 500 to make a three-digit number, i.e. 537. Similarly, children can separate a 3-digit number into its constituent parts – so 629 becomes 600 and 20 and 9.

Use the cards to show what a number looks like when it has a 0 in the tens place, or in the units. If the child selects a hundreds card (400) and a units card (6), but no tens card, what does the number look like, e.g. 406?

Number line

This is an important image for helping children to order the numbers. Use the number line to count above 100, so that children can see the repetitive elements of the count. Then let children create a number line that goes up in tens: 110, 120, 130, ... 200, 210, 220, ... This helps children to see the pattern. Adding a unit is then relatively simple.

Base ten equipment

If a child is experiencing difficulties with 3-digit numbers, base ten equipment with its entirely classroom context may not always help. There is some evidence that some children fail to transfer their grasp of the base ten equipment to an understanding of the structure of numbers. That is to say, they can manipulate the equipment, but they still can't manipulate numbers.

It can therefore help to make your own equipment, using sweets (10 sweets in a packet, and 100 sweets in a box) or football cards (10 in a packet, and 10 packets in a box) which will be more meaningful.

3-digit numbers

Activities

Note: All the activities can be undertaken either by individuals or by small groups. The activities are given in increasing order of difficulty.

ACTIVITY **1**

Place-value cards (hundreds, tens and units)
The children use the place-value cards to make three columns: the hundreds in order (100 to 900), the tens in order (10 to 90), the units in order (1 to 9). They should make sure that the cards are aligned in rows (i.e. 100 next to 10 next to 1).
They compare the three columns. What is the fourth number in the first column? 400. What is the fourth number in the second column? 40, etc.

ACTIVITY **2**

Place-value cards (hundreds, tens and units)
Shuffle the cards separately, and place them face up in three piles (hundreds, tens and units). Encourage the children to make five or six 2-digit numbers, using the tens and units cards, e.g. 60 and 3 to make 63. They should read these aloud to a helper.
Next they make 3-digit numbers, using the hundreds, tens and units cards. Again they should read the numbers aloud to a helper.
Start by focussing on matching the spoken number to the appropriate cards, e.g. *four hundred and sixty-seven* – 400 and 60 and 7, making 467.

ACTIVITY **3**

Base ten equipment
The children sort the base ten equipment into three sets: hundreds, tens and units. They take a handful of hundreds, and write the number, e.g. 400. They take some tens and place them with the hundreds, writing the new number, e.g. 460. Finally they add a handful of units, and write the new number, e.g. 465.
Repeat five times.

ACTIVITY **4**

Place-value cards (hundreds, tens and units)
Shuffle the cards separately, and place them face up in three piles (hundreds, tens and units). The children take one card from each pile (e.g. 400, 80, 5) and make a 3-digit number (485). They take another card from each pile (e.g. 200, 20, 4) and make another number (224). Which number is largest? They arrange the numbers to form a 'ladder', with the larger number at the top.
They continue choosing cards and making numbers, placing each one in its appropriate place on the ladder.

ACTIVITY **5**

Three dice
The children throw the three dice (e.g. 4, 6, 2), make a 3-digit number (462) and write it down.
They repeat ten times, and then write the numbers in order from largest to smallest.

Photocopy masters
Numeracy Support Book
pages 28 to 31

Associated units
Abacus 4 R4 Number

③ Adding tens

Strategies

Step 1 Rehearse counting in tens. Start with a number in the twenties, emphasising the rhyming aspect of these numbers: *twenty-**six**, thirty-**six**, forty-**six**, fifty-**six**,* ... Ensure that the children can count in tens from any number in the twenties.

Step 2 Count on ten from a 1-digit number or a number between 10 and 20. This is more difficult because of the lack of rhyme. Do **not** count on in ones. Demonstrate additions such as 4 + 10 = 14 using 10p and 1p coins or by moving down a column on a number grid.

Step 3 Start with any 2-digit number and add ten. Use the chant to help, e.g. 43 + 10 = *twenty-three, thirty-three, **forty**-three, **fifty**-three.*

Step 4 Add multiples of ten, using fingers to represent each ten, e.g. 43 + 30 =

Tactics

Chanting

Chanting the numbers, starting with a number in the twenties and adding ten each time, is certainly the best method of learning to add ten. Children should specifically **not** count on ten ones. Once the children have learned the chant: *twenty-three, thirty-three, forty-three,* ... they can use this to enable them to add ten to any number above 20. The numbers below 20 are more difficult, because they do not fit the rhyme or rhythm. When the children are confident counting in tens from any number above 20, they can tackle those below 20.

Fingers

Once children have learned the chant by heart they can use this knowledge to help them add ten or add a multiple of ten. They must do two things:

(i) Find the correct place in the chant to start. For example, for 38 + 10 = they need to find 38 in the 28, 38, 48, 58 chant.

(ii) Count on the requisite number of tens. For 38 + 10 = they need to count on one ten (one place in the chant), thirty-eight, forty-eight.

Fingers can help children to keep track of how **many** tens they are counting on. For example, for 41 + 30, the children must count on three tens (i.e. thirty) so they hold up three fingers. They find the correct starting place in the chant – *forty-one,* and then count on in tens, folding down one finger for each number spoken, *fifty-one, sixty-one, seventy-one.*

Calculators

The calculator can help children to see the pattern of counting in tens. They can enter a number in the twenties, and then add ten, write down the total and add ten again. The calculator allows them to focus on the pattern in the totals, rather than being confused by the actual arithmetic.

Writing chains of numbers provides good written practice, but there is no substitute for oral repetition for learning the tens by heart.

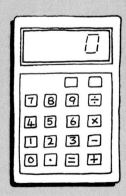

Adding tens

Activities

Note: All the activities can be undertaken either by individuals or by small groups. The activities are given in increasing order of difficulty.

ACTIVITY **1** **Number cards (1 to 100)**
Spread out the cards face up on the table. The children make a line of numbers which increase in tens, e.g. 22, 32, ... 92. How long can they make the line?
They should make three or four lines, each one as long as possible.

ACTIVITY **2** **10p and 1p coins (ten of each), a cloth or paper bag, 12 blank labels**
Place the money in the bag and shake it up. The children remove a small handful of coins, and count the total. They write the amount on one side of a label. They add another 10p coin, and write the new amount on the reverse of the label.
The children return the coins to the bag and repeat.

ACTIVITY **3** **Number cards (1 to 100)**
Spread out the cards face up on the table. The children take a card (e.g. 53), read the number aloud (*fifty-three*) and find the card that is ten more (63). They place the two cards together and write the matching addition, 53 + 10 = 63. They complete twelve additions.

ACTIVITY **4** **Two dice, five 10p coins in a cup**
The children throw the two dice (e.g. 3, 5), make a 2-digit number (35) and write it down. They tip the coins out of the cup and count how many land heads (e.g. 3). They add that number of tens (30) to the original number, writing the matching addition, 35 + 30 = 65.
They repeat for twelve additions.

ACTIVITY **5** **A number grid (1 to 100), coloured cubes**
The children start by choosing a number in the 'teens', e.g. 16. They add ten and place a red cube on the answer on the number grid (i.e. 26). They next add twenty to the original number and put a blue cube on the answer (36). They continue, adding ten more and placing a cube on the answer.
They repeat for three or four new 'teen' numbers.
The children clear the grid, and start again with a 1-digit number, adding ten and placing a coloured cube on the answer. They should try three or four like this.

Photocopy masters
Numeracy Support Book
pages 32 to 35

Associated units
Abacus 4 R2 Addition

4 Doubling

Strategies

Step 1 Rehearse doubles of numbers up to 10. *Two and two, three and three, four and four, ...* Use fingers to help with the numbers up to five. Then learn the doubles of 6 to 10, by chanting, as well as written repetition.

Step 2 Double the numbers from 10 to 15. Double the tens first, then the units. For example, double 13 – *ten and ten is twenty, and three and three is six. Twenty-six.*

Step 3 Double the multiples of ten up to 50. *Ten and ten, twenty and twenty, thirty and thirty, ...* Written practice helps to relate this to the doubles of 1 to 5.

Step 4 Double 2-digit numbers less than 50 whose units are 5 or less.

Step 5 Learn the doubles of the numbers which have 5 units up to 45.

Tactics

Fingers

Fingers are useful in helping children to double the numbers up to 5. They can hold up two fingers on each hand, *two and two makes four*, and repeat this process for 3 and 3, 4 and 4 etc. Then the children can use their fingers in a similar fashion to rehearse the doubles of the tens (where each finger stands for 10). *Ten and ten* – holding up one finger on each hand, *twenty and twenty* – two fingers on each hand, etc.

Money

Using money in a structured way can help to reinforce the process of doubling tens and units. Use coins to match the number to be doubled, starting with multiples of ten. 10p and 10p makes 20p, 20p and 20p makes 40p, and so on. Then move onto using 10p coins and one or two 1p coins. For example, double 12p (one 10p and two 1p coins). *First double the tens – take another 10p coin. Then double the units – take two more 1p coins. Two tens and four ones. Twenty-four pence.* Repeat this process, always with a units digit less than 5.

Base ten equipment

This can be used in the same way as money, to reinforce the process of doubling the tens and then the units. Start with the multiples of ten, ensuring that these are memorised. Then continue with numbers under 50, with a units digit less than 5. For example double 31 (three rods and one unit). *Take three more rods, and one more unit.* Combine all the rods and units. *There are now six rods and two units – sixty-two.*

Calculator

Use a calculator to help the children recognise the doubles of the multiples of five, e.g. double 25. Enter 25 on the calculator and press + 25. This reinforces the idea of doubling as adding the same amount again. Write the first number: 25, and the answer when it is added to itself: 50. Double all the numbers between 5 and 50 in this way. Look at the patterns. Focus on the numbers ending in 5. Memorise by chanting.

Doubling

Activities

Note: All the activities can be undertaken either by individuals or by small groups. The activities are given in increasing order of difficulty.

ACTIVITY 1

Number cards (1 to 10), lots of cubes

Spread out the cards face down on the table. The children turn over a card (e.g. 3) and double the number (6). They take a matching number of cubes, build them in to a tower and place them with the card. They continue until all the cards have been picked and matched. The children then check the doubles, by splitting each tower into two equal halves, and counting the cubes in one half. The cubes should match the number on the card.

ACTIVITY 2

Number grid 3 (Resource Pack PCM), base ten equipment, some small Post-it Notes

The children choose a number on the grid and double it, using fingers or base ten equipment to help. They write the answer on a Post-it Note and stick it over the number on the grid.

They continue for each number on the grid.

ACTIVITY 3

Twenty 10p coins, a cup, labels with the multiples of tens: 10, 20, 30 to 200

The children place 12 coins in the cup, shake it and tip them out. They remove the coins that land tails, and then double the remainder (using other coins to help). They find the matching label with the answer on it. For example, three coins land heads, double 30 is 60, find the label with 60 on it.

They repeat the process starting with another 12 coins in the cup. The children continue until they have matched six different labels. *Why can't certain labels be matched?*

ACTIVITY 4

Number grid 2, blank number grid (Resource Pack PCMs), base ten equipment

The children choose a number on the grid (e.g. 19) and match it with base ten equipment (one rod and nine units). They take exactly the same number of rods and units again, and find the total (they may have to exchange ten units for one rod). They write the double on the matching space on the blank grid.

The children continue, until each number on the grid has been doubled.

Photocopy masters

Numeracy Support Book
pages 36 to 40

Associated units

Abacus 4 N5 Multiplication

5 Fractions

Strategies

Children's confusion about fractions usually arises in recognising a fraction both as a part of a whole and as a quantity. Children sometimes find it difficult to relate the notion of one half of a circle to 10 out of 20 beads, for example.

Step 1 Demonstrate one half as one of two equal pieces, and one quarter as one of four equal pieces.

Step 2 Find one half or one quarter of a variety of different single objects, e.g. a piece of paper, a length of string, an apple.

Step 3 Show that one half of an apple is the same as two quarters.

Step 4 Use a 'cake' to link one half of a whole to one half of a quantity. Stick 12 'sweets' around the edge of the 'cake'. Cut it in half – six sweets in each half. Cut it into quarters – 3 sweets in each quarter.

Step 5 Find one half, one quarter and three quarters of small numbers.

Tactics

Cakes

Dividing circular or square 'cakes' is the easiest and most visual way of approaching halves and quarters. If at all possible, start with a real cake, and move on to a 'cake' made from thin card. Fold and cut the cake as shown.

Use the cake to show that one quarter, one half, or three quarters have been eaten, by folding and writing the relevant fractions.

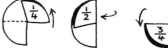

Introduce the idea of halving a quantity by making a cake with twelve sweets around the edge, evenly spaced. How many sweets are there in one quarter? How many are there in one half? How many in three quarters? Make different cakes, with different numbers of sweets, and fold and label as before.

Interlocking cubes

Use interlocking cubes to build a strip of, for example, twelve cubes. Split the strip into two halves. *How many cubes in each half?* Divide each half in half again, to make four matching strips. *How many cubes in each quarter?* Place the strips side by side so they are clearly the same size. *Four quarters. Three cubes in each.*

The strips can be used to demonstrate to the children that one quarter can be found by halving and then halving again. The strips also emphasise that all the quarters of a quantity are the same, because all the strips are the same length.

Fractions

Activities

Note: All the activities can be undertaken either by individuals or by small groups. The activities are given in increasing order of difficulty.

ACTIVITY ❶

A piece of string, an apple, a cake, a pile of sand, a plastic straw, a strip of eight interlocking cubes, a piece of paper, twelve 1p coins
The children divide each item in half. Discuss how each half must be the same. They then halve each half again to make quarters.
Note: the children might need help cutting the cake and the apple.

ACTIVITY ❷

A variety of paper shapes, felt-tipped pens
The children fold each shape in half, then in half again. They open the shapes out and colour the quarters differently. Discuss how all the quarters of each shape are the same size.

ACTIVITY ❸

A thin card circle, small stickers, felt-tipped pens, scissors
The children fold the circle in half, then half again, and colour the quarters differently. They make a radial cut, then fold the first quarter and write '$\frac{1}{4}$' on the back. They fold the second quarter and write '$\frac{1}{2}$' on the back. They fold the third quarter and write '$\frac{3}{4}$' on the back.
They can use the small stickers to stick sweets on their cake. Start with one sticker in each quarter. *Four sweets on the cake. How many in a quarter? How many in a half?* Stick one more sweet in each quarter. *Eight sweets on the cake. How many in a quarter? How many in a half?* The children continue adding more sweets.

ACTIVITY ❹

Interlocking cubes
Build strips of 12, 16, 20 and 24 cubes, each strip a different colour. The children choose a strip, count how many cubes, e.g. 12, and write it down. They divide the strip into two halves. *How many cubes in each half?* They write it: $\frac{1}{2}$ of 12 is 6.
They divide each half in half again. *Four small matching strips. Four quarters. How many cubes in each quarter?* They write it: $\frac{1}{4}$ of 12 is 3. Continue for the remaining strips.

ACTIVITY ❺

Six small rectangular grids, drawn on squared paper (each with an area that is a multiple of four), felt-tipped pens
The children choose a grid and count how many squares. They colour one quarter. They choose another grid, count how many squares and colour one half. They choose a third grid, count how many squares and colour three quarters.
Repeat for the remaining three grids.

Photocopy masters

Numeracy Support Book
pages 41 to 44

Associated units

Abacus 4 R3 Fractions

6 Rounding

Strategies

Step 1 Make a number line from 1 to 20. Use this to find the nearest ten (or zero) to any number on the line.

Step 2 Extend the number line to 50. Use the same tactic to find the nearest ten (or zero) to any number on the line.

Step 3 Extend the number line to 100. Use this to find the nearest ten (or zero) to any number on the line.

Step 4 Encourage the children to focus on the units digit. If the units digit is 5 or more, round up to the next ten. If the units digit is 4 or less, round down to the previous ten. Encourage the children to judge which ten the number is closest to. Rounding up is often easier than rounding down, so start with numbers that can be rounded up to give the children confidence. Then move to numbers with 1, 2, 3 or 4 as the units digit.

Tactics

Number line

This is obviously a significant image in helping children to grasp the idea of rounding up and rounding down. It is very important at the start that the children make their own number lines, using large numbers made out of sugar paper and stuck on the table with Blu-Tack.

At first, make the number line up to 20, then extend it to 30 and then 50. There are two stages to the process of using the number line:
(i) The children need to look for the nearest number ending in 0.
(ii) They need to recognise which ten is nearer, the next ten or the previous ten.

Money

The children can match numbers with 10p and 1p coins. They look at the number of units (1p coins). Are there more or less than 5? If there are less than five, take them away. If there are five or more, add another 10p and remove the 1p coins. For example, 38, lay out three 10p and eight 1p coins. There are more than five 1p coins, so add another 10p and remove the 1p coins, leaving four 10p coins – 40p.

Encourage the children to realise that they are looking for the nearest number of 10p coins. *If you didn't have any 1p coins, how many 10p coins would be the nearest amount?*

Rounding

Activities

Note: All the activities can be undertaken either by individuals or by small groups. The activities are given in increasing order of difficulty.

ACTIVITY ① **Lots of 10p and 1p coins in a cloth or paper bag, labels with the multiples of ten**

The children place the labels in a line in order. They shake the bag of coins, and remove a small amount. They lay out the coins and count the total, e.g. 48p, writing the number.

They check the number of 1p coins. If there are five or more, they take another 10p and return the 1p coins to the bag. If there are fewer than five, they simply return the 1p coins to the bag. They count the final amount (i.e. 50p), and write it down.

The children return all the coins to the bag and repeat at least ten times.

ACTIVITY ② **Number cards (15 to 19, 25 to 29, ... 95 to 99), labels with the multiples of ten, a number line (1 to 100) can be helpful**

Shuffle the cards and place them face down in a pile. The children turn over a card, e.g. 27, round it to the nearest ten (30) and place it with the appropriate label.

They repeat for each card in the pile.

ACTIVITY ③ **Number cards (11 to 14, 21 to 24, ... 91 to 94), labels with the multiples of ten, a number line (1 to 100) can be helpful**

Repeat Activity 2 but with children rounding down rather than rounding up.

ACTIVITY ④ **Number cards (11 and 19, 21 and 29, ... 91 and 99), labels with the multiples of ten**

Shuffle the cards and place them face down in a pile. Place the multiples of ten in a line in order, well spaced. The children turn over a card, and round it to its nearest ten. They place it with the appropriate label.

They continue revealing cards, rounding and placing with the appropriate label. When all the cards have been taken there should be two cards under each multiple.

ACTIVITY ⑤ **Number cards (1 to 100), a pad of Post-it Notes**

Shuffle the cards and place them face down in a pile. The children turn over the top card and decide whether to round it up or down – are there five or more units? They round it up or down as appropriate, write the nearest ten on a Post-it Note and stick it on the card.

They continue until they have labelled at least twelve cards correctly.

Photocopy masters

Numeracy Support Book
pages 45 to 48

7 Estimating the sum

Strategies

Step 1 Rehearse adding multiples of ten. First count in multiples of ten: *Ten, twenty, thirty, forty, ...* Then rehearse adding the multiples, e.g. 30 + 40 =.

Step 2 Rehearse rounding up and down to the nearest ten (see Section 6).

Step 3 Read the addition, e.g. 32 + 47 = as: *Thirty-two add forty-seven is...?*

Step 4 Focus on the first number. Round this up or down to its nearest ten. Then focus on the second number. Round this up or down to the nearest ten.

Step 5 Add the two multiples of ten. Emphasise that this is an approximate answer. Compare with the total found on a calculator.

Tactics

Money

Money provides the most helpful method of estimating, because it makes sense to ignore the 1p coins. The children first of all read the addition, e.g. 38 + 51 =, as: *Thirty-eight add fifty-one is...?* If they can, the children round each number to its nearest ten and write the approximations, i.e. 40 + 50 =, matching each amount with 10p coins.

If the children can't round up or down straight away, they match each amount exactly with 10p and 1p coins. If there are more than five 1p coins, they take another 10p and remove the 1p coins. If there are fewer than five, they simply remove the 1p coins.

The number of 10p coins then gives an approximate answer.

Number line

The image of the number line not only helps with the rounding aspects of the estimation but also with the addition. The children find the first number on the line, and then move to its nearest ten, writing it down. They find the second number on the line, and then move to its nearest ten, writing it down. They add the two multiples of ten, using the number line if necessary.

Number grid (1 to 100)

The number grid helps those children having difficulty adding multiples of ten. It can also help with the rounding up or down. The children look at the first number in the addition, and find it on the grid. This part is important – help the children to get a sense of where the numbers appear in the grid. Do they start in approximately the correct place, or are they unsure of where to start looking? Using the grid breeds a familiarity that is extremely helpful in many number activities.

The children round the numbers up or down and write the new addition. For example 62 + 27 is approximately 60 + 30. They can then use the number grid to help them complete the addition.

Estimating the sum

Activities

Note: All the activities can be undertaken either by individuals or by small groups. The activities are given in increasing order of difficulty.

ACTIVITY **1**

Place-value cards (10, 20, ... 50)

Spread out the cards face up. The children pick two cards and add them, writing the addition, e.g. 20 + 50 = 70. How many **different** additions can they complete using pairs of cards from the table? They should write each one down.

ACTIVITY **2**

Number cards (1 to 50), a pad of Post-it Notes, a calculator

Spread out the cards face down. The children turn over a pair of cards, e.g. 49 and 23. They round each number to its nearest ten, and complete the addition, writing it down, i.e. 50 + 20 = 70. They write the answer on a Post-it Note and place it with the two cards.
The children continue until all the cards have been taken. They then use the calculator to find the exact total for each pair, comparing with their estimates.

ACTIVITY **3**

Two dice

The children throw the two dice (e.g. 2 and 6), and write down a 2-digit number, e.g. 26. They throw the two dice again, and write down a second 2-digit number, e.g. 43. The children round each number to its nearest ten (26 → 30 and 43 → 40) and complete the addition, writing the total, i.e. 30 + 40 = 70.
The children repeat for at least six additions.

ACTIVITY **4**

Number cards (1 to 9), a calculator

Spread the cards out face up. The children pick four cards (e.g. 1, 2, 5, 8) and arrange them to make two 2-digit numbers, e.g. 12 and 58. They write the matching addition, i.e. 12 + 58 =. The children round each number to its nearest ten (12 → 10, 58 → 60) and complete the addition, writing the total, i.e. 10 + 60 = 70. They check on the calculator.
The children replace the cards and repeat several times. Can they make two numbers that add up to approximately 50?

Photocopy masters

Numeracy Support Book
pages 49 to 52

8 Subtraction

Strategies

Children often find it easier to add than to subtract. This is related to the fact that it is much easier to count on than to count back. It is also clear that subtraction in everyday life often requires that we count on (e.g. when giving or checking change). Therefore, for children who are finding subtraction difficult, counting on can be a valuable approach.

Step 1 Rehearse the use of the number line. Use a number line up to 20, and let the children make their own from cut-out numbers.

Step 2 Read a subtraction such as 13 – 8 = as an addition with missing numbers. *How far is it from 8 to 13? Eight and how many more make thirteen?* Practise reading subtractions like this.

Step 3 Use the number line to assist the counting on. Hold up one finger for each number spoken. Start at 8, and count on to 13: *Nine, ten, ... thirteen. Five fingers. We count on five to get from 8 to 13. Eight and five more make thirteen. 13 – 8 = 5.*

Step 4 Emphasise that subtraction is about finding how much we have to add to get from the second number to the first. Read 15 – 9 = as: *How many is it from nine to fifteen?* or: *How many do we add to nine to get fifteen?*

Tactics

Number line or track

The number line provides the simplest visual means of showing subtraction as difference. Finding how many steps there are between 9 and 15 is best assisted by a number line or track.

Produce a bank of photocopied tracks. Read a subtraction such as 15 – 9 as: *How far is it from 9 to 15?* or: *How many steps from 9 to 15?* The children can put one finger on the 9, and then mark with a pencil each space on the track as they count up to 15 (including 15). *How many spots? Six. It is six steps from 9 to 15. 15 – 9 = 6.*

Money

Money can be useful, in terms of motivation, and also in its use outside the classroom. Phrase subtractions such as 14 – 8 = as: *How much more do you have if you have 14p and I have 8p?* Start with 8p and count on, in this instance by adding 1p coins, until there is 14p in total. Keep the additional 1p coins in a separate pile. *How many did you add?*

It is best to use real money (you only need about twenty 1p coins).

Interlocking cubes

Strips of interlocking cubes can be useful in helping children move from one amount to another. Read 13 – 9 = as: *How many more bricks do I have to add to a strip of nine to make it thirteen cubes long?*

The children start with a strip of nine cubes, in one colour. They add cubes of another colour until it is thirteen cubes long. *How many cubes did they add?*

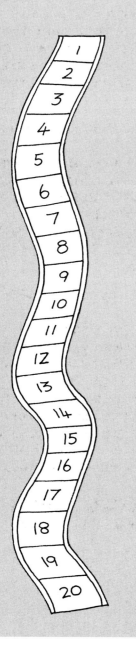

Subtraction

Activities

Note: All the activities can be undertaken either by individuals or by small groups. The activities are given in increasing order of difficulty.

ACTIVITY ❶

Large number track (1 to 20), small cubes or counters
Give the children a subtraction, e.g. 14 – 7 =. Starting at the second number, they should count along the track placing a cube on each space up to (and including) 14. How many cubes have they put on the track? Repeat for 10 subtractions.

ACTIVITY ❷

Lots of 1p coins, some labels with subtractions (numbers all less than 20) written on them
Shuffle the labels and place them face down in a pile. The children turn over one, e.g. 12 – 5 = and read it as: *How much do I need to add to 5p to make 12p?* They make a pile of 5p coins, then add coins one at a time to a separate pile, counting on as they do so: *six, seven, … twelve.* How many coins have been added? Seven. They write 7 on the back of the label.
The children continue for each label in turn. When all the labels are complete, they can shuffle them and place them face up, then try to say which number is on the back of each.

ACTIVITY ❸

Number cards (1 to 20), interlocking cubes (in two colours, e.g. red and yellow)
Shuffle the cards and spread them out face down. The children turn over two cards (e.g. 4 and 11), and write a matching subtraction with the larger number first (11 – 4 =). They build a strip of red cubes to match the smaller number, then add yellow cubes until the strip matches the larger number. How many cubes have they added? Seven. Complete the subtraction: 11 – 4 = 7.
The children repeat for different pairs of cards.

ACTIVITY ❹

Number track (1 to 20), a dice, two differently coloured cubes (e.g. red and yellow)
The children start by placing the red cube on 20 and the yellow cube on 1. They throw the dice (e.g. 6) and move the yellow cube along the track a matching number of spaces (i.e. to 7). They throw the dice again (e.g. 4) and move the red cube back a matching number of spaces (i.e. to 16). The children write a subtraction to match the positions of the cubes (16 – 7 =). They find the answer by counting on from the yellow cube to the red cube, holding up one finger for each number spoken: *eight, nine, ten, … sixteen.* Nine fingers. 16 – 7 = 9.
The children replace the cubes on 1 and 20 and repeat at least ten times.

Photocopy masters
Numeracy Support Book
pages 53 to 56

Associated units
Abacus 4 N2 Subtraction

9 ×5 table

(and rehearsal of ×2 and ×10)

Strategies

Step 1 The children should memorise the chant: *Five, ten, fifteen, twenty, ... fifty.*

Step 2 Match the chant to a finger-count, holding up one finger for each number. *Five* (holding up one finger), *ten* (two fingers), etc.

Step 3 Once the children are confident counting in fives, alert their attention to 'how many' fives. Stop the chant part way through and look at how many fingers. *Five, ten, fifteen, twenty. Four fingers. Four fives are twenty.*

Step 4 Find any ×5 table fact by counting silently along with fingers. For example: *Six fives are ... ?* Chant silently: *five, ten, fifteen, ... thirty* (six fingers standing up). *Six fives are thirty.*

Tactics

Money

Use 5p coins to help the children count in fives. As with fingers, coins can be used alongside the chant to help children recognise **how many** fives they have counted. So when chanting: *Five, ten, fifteen, twenty, ...* take a coin for each number spoken. Stop at twenty. *Four coins. Four fives are twenty.*

Money also supplies a physical reality to the 'fiveness' of counting in fives. Each 5p coin is worth five 1p coins (so for example, I could buy five one penny chews). Similarly, 2p coins can be used to help the children learn the ×2 table, and 10p coins to help with the ×10 table.

Chanting

The key skill at this stage is that children memorise the multiples of five by repetition. It is the oral practice that is crucial here. There is a rhyming quality to the list of multiples of five and ten that is a great help: *Five, ten, fifteen, **twenty**, twenty-**five**, **thirty**, thirty-**five**, **forty**, ...* Stress the rhyme, and chant in a steady rhythm.

Make a tape recording of the chants and count along to it, pointing to the numbers in a list of multiples at the same time. So, with the multiples in front of them: 2, 4, 6, 8, ... 20, the children can chant the numbers aloud: *Two, four, six, ... twenty.* They can put a small coloured sticker by each number as they say its name.

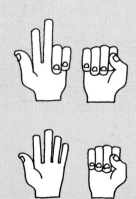

Fingers

As the above strategies suggest, fingers are an extremely useful tactic in helping children find a tables fact. The same method outlined in the strategies can equally be used for the ×2 and ×10 tables. Use the chant alongside the fingers-count: *two, four, six, ... ten,* holding up one finger for each number. Stop the chant and look at how many fingers: *five twos are ten.*

Once the children are familiar with this method, it becomes second nature for them to use fingers to find any ×2, ×5 or ×10 tables fact.

×5 table

(and rehearsal of ×2 and ×10)

Activities

Note: All the activities can be undertaken either by individuals or by small groups. The activities are given in increasing order of difficulty.

ACTIVITY ①

Number cards (1 to 50), small pieces of coloured card, a needle, wool
Spread out the number cards face up on the table. The children select all the multiples of five, and place them in order from 5 to 50. They copy each number onto a piece of card, then thread all the cards together in order. The children can hang this where it will help to remind them how to count in fives.
The activity can be repeated for the multiples of two or ten.

ACTIVITY ②

Ten 5p coins in a cup
The children shake the cup, tip out the coins and count those that are heads, e.g. 4. They write a matching multiplication, i.e. 4 × 5 =, and write the answer: 20.
The children return the coins to the cup and repeat. They should continue for ten multiplications.
The activity can be repeated using 2p or 10p coins.

ACTIVITY ③

Lots of interlocking cubes, sticky labels
The children make a model using up to ten cubes. If each cube were worth 5p, how much would the model cost? The children find the total amount, write the answer on a label, and stick it on the model. They repeat for at least eight models (each made with a different number of cubes).
The activity can be repeated with cubes worth 2p or 10p each.

ACTIVITY ④

Number cards (5, 10, 15, ... 50), a counter, a dice
Arrange the cards face up in a circle. The children select one, and place the counter on it. They throw the dice and move clockwise around the circle of cards to, for example, 40. *How many fives make 40? There are eight fives in 40.* The children take eight cubes, make a strip and place it beside the card.
They continue playing, until each card has at least one strip of cubes.

ACTIVITY ⑤

Lots of cubes, sticky labels, a calculator
The children make models using only red, blue and yellow cubes. If red cubes were worth 2p, blue cubes 5p and yellow cubes 10p, how much would the model cost? The children find the total amount, write the answer on a label, and stick it on the model. They use the calculator to help with the addition. They repeat for different models.

ACTIVITY ⑥

The children invent a rap for the ×5 table. *Five alive, ten in the den, moving on to fifteen, what do you mean? I mean twenty, that's half empty...* When they are happy with it they should record it onto tape to help them memorise the ×5 table.
They can invent other raps for the ×2 or ×10 tables.

Photocopy masters

Numeracy Support Book
pages 57 to 60

⑩ Division

Strategies

If children have not understood division by Abacus 4, it is likely that the idea of 'sharing' has not been a helpful explanation. An alternative strategy is to describe division in terms of its relation to multiplication.

Step 1 Rehearse multiplication, using the notion of 'rows of'. Read 3×4 as: *Three rows of four.* Start with small numbers (up to 6×6).

Step 2 Present division as 'multiplications with missing numbers'. Suggest that $12 \div 4$ is read as: *How many fours in 12?*

Step 3 Draw rows of buns or crosses to find the missing numbers. For example, for $12 \div 4$, start with a row of four buns. Continue drawing rows of four buns until there are twelve buns in total. *How many rows are there? Three.* $12 \div 4 = 3$.

Step 4 Emphasise that '$20 \div 4 =$' is read as: *How many fours in twenty?*

Tactics

Drawing rows

Both division and multiplication are best visualised by children having difficulty with these concepts as 'rows of buns'. Thus 3×5 is represented as three rows of five buns, and the total counted, preferably in rows: *Five, ten, fifteen.* $3 \times 5 = 15$.

Similarly $15 \div 5$ can be depicted as fifteen buns in rows of five. $15 \div 5$ asks us: *How many fives in fifteen?* The children start by drawing a row of five buns. They add rows of five buns, counting as they do so: *Five, ten, ...* When they have drawn fifteen buns they count the number of rows. *Three rows.* $15 \div 5 = 3$.

Squared paper

Rectangles drawn on squared paper can be used in a similar fashion to the 'rows of buns' described above. The advantage of using squared paper is that rows of the equal number will also be the same **length**. When children draw buns, the rows may not look the same length and may not be reliably ordered, which can lead to errors, especially as the numbers get larger. The disadvantage of using squared paper is that it is much more abstract than the 'rows of buns' which children create themselves.

When using squared paper, the children simply draw round and then cut out the requisite number of rows. For example, 2×6 is read as: *Two rows of six.* The children draw two rows of six squares, $2 \times 6 = 12$.

Similarly, '$12 \div 6$' is read as: *How many sixes in 12?* The children draw two rows of six squares, $12 \div 6 = 2$.

Lists of multiples

Once confident drawing and counting rows of equal length children can move on to dispense with this visual image. At this point they can simply produce the necessary lists of multiples, counting in twos, threes, fours etc. For example, they read '$14 \div 2 =$' as: *How many twos in fourteen?* They count in twos, using fingers (holding up one finger for each number spoken) or writing a list: 2, 4, 6, ... 14. *Seven fingers. Seven numbers in the list. Seven twos are fourteen.* $14 \div 2 = 7$.

Division

Activities

Note: All the activities can be undertaken either by individuals or by small groups. The activities are given in increasing order of difficulty.

ACTIVITY **1**

Number cards (2, 4, 6, ... 30)

Shuffle the cards and place them face down in a pile. The children turn over the top card, e.g. 16. *How many twos are in this number?* The children write down the division, 16 ÷ 2 =, and draw buns in rows of two to find the answer. *Eight rows of two. 16 ÷ 2 = 8.*
The children continue, completing divisions for at least ten cards.

ACTIVITY **2**

Number cards (1 to 30)

The children place the cards in a line, in order. They choose any number ending in '5' or '0' (e.g. 15) and divide it by 5. *How many fives in fifteen?* They write the division: 15 ÷ 5, and draw buns in rows of five to find the answer. *Three rows of five. 15 ÷ 5 = 3.*
The children continue, completing divisions for at least five cards.

ACTIVITY **3**

Cards with simple divisions written on them (e.g. 10 ÷ 2, 8 ÷ 4, 6 ÷ 3, 12 ÷ 6, 14 ÷ 2), interlocking cubes

Shuffle the cards and place them face down in a pile.
The children turn over the top card, e.g. 10 ÷ 2, and build strips of interlocking cubes to match the division. For example they build strips of two cubes until there are ten cubes in total. *How many strips? Five.*
10 ÷ 2 = 5. The children write the answer on the back of the card.
They continue for each card in the pile.
When all the cards are complete the children can test themselves by looking at the front of the card and saying the answer on the back, without the help of cubes.

ACTIVITY **4**

Lists of multiples (×2, ×5, ×10), cards with simple divisions (÷ 2, ÷ 5, ÷ 10) written on them

Shuffle the division cards and place them face down in a pile.
The children turn over a division card, and decide which 'table' it relates to (looking at the second number to check). For example, 12 ÷ 2 means counting in twos to find the answer, using the multiples of two to help. *How many twos in twelve? Six.* The children write the answer on the back of the card.
They continue for each card in the pile.
When all the cards are complete the children can test themselves by looking at the front of the card and saying the answer on the back.

Photocopy masters

Numeracy Support Book
pages 61 to 64

Associated units

Abacus 4 R1 Multiplication, R5 Division

Name _____

Adding

Complete these.   Use fingers to help you.

$2 + 2 = \boxed{4}$

$5 + 5 = \boxed{}$ $3 + 3 = \boxed{}$ $6 + 6 = \boxed{}$

$1 + 1 = \boxed{}$ $4 + 4 = \boxed{}$ $7 + 7 = \boxed{}$

$10 + 10 = \boxed{}$ $8 + 8 = \boxed{}$ $9 + 9 = \boxed{}$

There are 10 birds in each nest.   How many have flown away?

$3 + \boxed{7} = 10$ $5 + \boxed{} = 10$ $2 + \boxed{} = 10$

$4 + \boxed{} = 10$ $1 + \boxed{} = 10$ $6 + \boxed{} = 10$

Name —————————————————————

Counting on

| 1 | 2 | 3 | 4 | 5 | 6 | 7 | 8 | 9 | 10 | 11 | 12 | 13 | 14 | 15 | 16 | 17 | 18 | 19 | 20 |

Complete these.　Use the track to help you.

$8 + 1 = \boxed{9}$

$11 + 1 = \boxed{}$　$15 + 1 = \boxed{}$　$17 + 1 = \boxed{}$

$7 + 1 = \boxed{}$　$4 + 1 = \boxed{}$　$18 + 1 = \boxed{}$

$20 + 1 = \boxed{}$　$10 + 1 = \boxed{}$　$13 + 1 = \boxed{}$

Each worm grows 2 more rings.　Write how many in total.

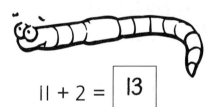

$11 + 2 = \boxed{13}$

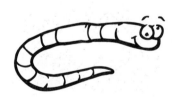

$12 + 2 = \boxed{}$

$6 + 2 = \boxed{}$

$9 + 2 = \boxed{}$

$10 + 2 = \boxed{}$

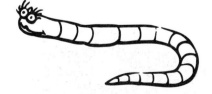

$16 + 2 = \boxed{}$

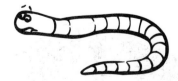

$17 + 2 = \boxed{}$

Name _____

Adding

Choose 2 balloons and write their prices. | Add them and write the total. | Write 10 different additions.

 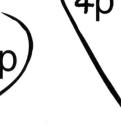 

15p 12p 16p 4p 19p 8p

18p 2p 17p 10p 5p

 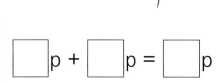

11p 13p 14p

☐p + ☐p = ☐p | ☐p + ☐p = ☐p | ☐p + ☐p = ☐p

☐p + ☐p = ☐p | ☐p + ☐p = ☐p

☐p + ☐p = ☐p | ☐p + ☐p = ☐p | ☐p + ☐p = ☐p

☐p + ☐p = ☐p | ☐p + ☐p = ☐p

Adding

Ali   **Fred**   **Sam**   **Mary**   **Dave**   **Zoe**

> Write how many conkers each pair has in total.

Sam and Ali

| 12 | + | 8 | = | 20 |

Ali   and   Fred

☐ + ☐ = ☐

Mary and Zoe

☐ + ☐ = ☐

Dave and Mary

☐ + ☐ = ☐

Fred and Mary

☐ + ☐ = ☐

Fred and Zoe

☐ + ☐ = ☐

Fred and Dave

☐ + ☐ = ☐

Sam and Zoe

☐ + ☐ = ☐

Sam and Mary

☐ + ☐ = ☐

Dave and Zoe

☐ + ☐ = ☐

Dave and Sam

☐ + ☐ = ☐

> Complete this addition table.

+	10	11	12	13	14	15
7	17					
9					23	

27

Counting

Write the missing numbers.

Start

| 249 | 250 | 251 | | |

| 261 | 260 | | | 257 | | 255 |

| | | | | 269 | 270 | 271 |

| 280 | | | | | | |

| 281 | | | | | 287 | | | |

Throws   ① ② ③ ④ ⑤ ⑥ ⑦ ⑧ ⑨ ⑩

Place a counter at the start.

Throw a dice and move around the track.

How many throws to reach the end?

28

Counting

Continue the
lines of numbers.

34 35 36 37 38 39 40

134 135 136

251 252 253

367 368 369

487 488 489

596 597 598

626 627 628

748 749

Counting

Each card hides 2 numbers on the track.

Write the missing numbers.

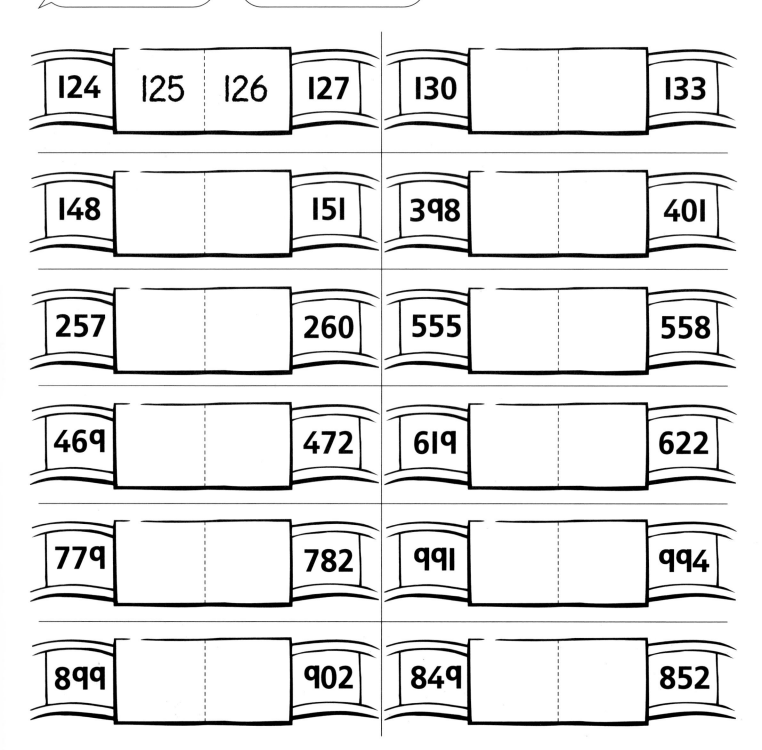

| 124 | 125 | 126 | 127 |
| 130 | | | 133 |

| 148 | | | 151 |
| 398 | | | 401 |

| 257 | | | 260 |
| 555 | | | 558 |

| 469 | | | 472 |
| 619 | | | 622 |

| 779 | | | 782 |
| 991 | | | 994 |

| 899 | | | 902 |
| 849 | | | 852 |

Counting

Choose a hundreds card and a number card. — Add them. — Write 10 additions.

| 500 | 300 | 54 | 78 | 69 |
| 800 | 21 | 33 | 40 | 17 |

500	+	69	=	569		☐	+	☐	=	☐
☐	+	☐	=	☐		☐	+	☐	=	☐
☐	+	☐	=	☐		☐	+	☐	=	☐
☐	+	☐	=	☐		☐	+	☐	=	☐
☐	+	☐	=	☐		☐	+	☐	=	☐

Write these numbers in order from smallest to largest.

704   407
247   742   207   472

Adding 10

> Continue the lines of numbers.

> Add 10 each time.

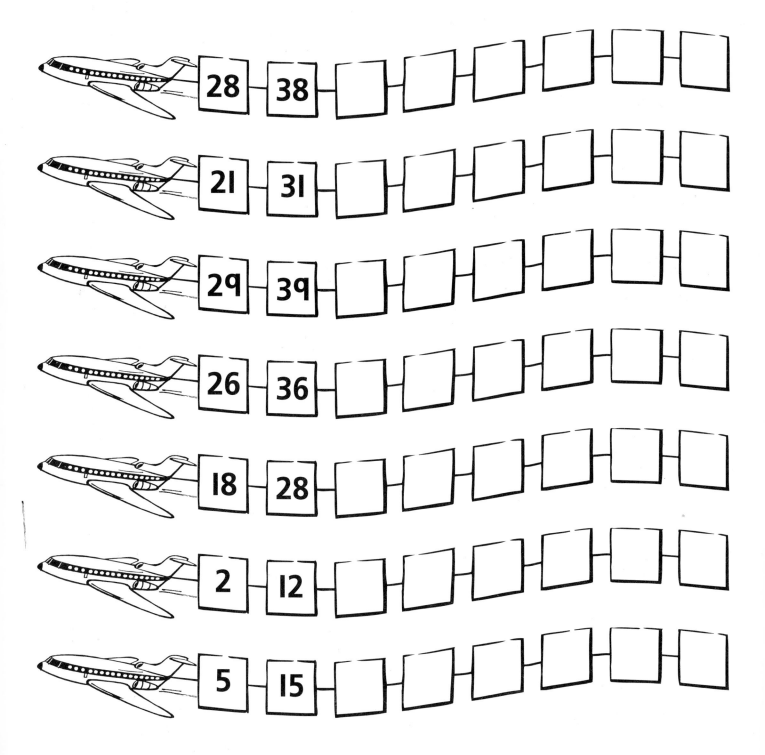

		28	38						
21	31						
29	39						
26	36						
18	28						
2	12						
5	15						

Name —————————————————————

Adding 10

Add 10 to each card.

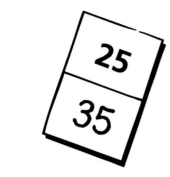 25 / 35

 54

 40

 48

 39

 66

 75

 82

 16

21

 19

52

33

61

14

 77

 90

7

Name _____

Adding 10, 20 ...

Add 10p to each money box. | Write the new totals.

 **62p**

total: [72] p

 **54p**

total: [ ] p

 **88p**

total: [ ] p

 **13p**

total: [ ] p

 **20p**

total: [ ] p

 **76p**

total: [ ] p

 **8p**

total: [ ] p

 **11p**

total: [ ] p

 **2p**

total: [ ] p

Complete this addition table.

+	43	28	71	89	70	16	37	45
10	53							
20								

Name _____

Adding 10, 20, 30 …

Each item goes up 20p.　Write the new prices.

 **49p**

49p + 20p = ☐ p

 **34p**

34p + 20p = ☐ p

 **67p**

67p + 20p = ☐ p

 **40p**

40p + 20p = ☐ p

 **82p**

82p + 20p = ☐ p

17p

17p + 20p = ☐ p

Each snake grows 30 cm.　Write the new lengths.

59 cm + 30 cm = ☐ cm

28 cm + 30 cm = ☐ cm

63 cm + 30 cm = ☐ cm

76 cm + 30 cm = ☐ cm

Name _____

Doubling

Complete these. Use fingers to help you.

 3 + 3 = ☐

 5 + 5 = ☐

 4 + 4 = ☐

 2 + 2 = ☐

 7 + 7 = ☐

 8 + 8 = ☐

 1 + 1 = ☐

 6 + 6 = ☐

 9 + 9 = ☐

 10 + 10 = ☐

12 + 12 = ☐

11 + 11 = ☐

Doubling

Double the money
in each purse.

10 + 10 = ☐

2 + 2 = ☐

total: ☐ p

10 + 10 = ☐

1 + 1 = ☐

total: ☐ p

10 + 10 = ☐

3 + 3 = ☐

total: ☐ p

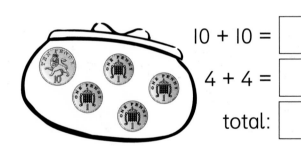

10 + 10 = ☐

4 + 4 = ☐

total: ☐ p

10 + 10 = ☐

5 + 5 = ☐

total: ☐ p

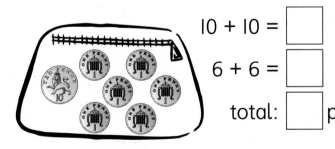

10 + 10 = ☐

6 + 6 = ☐

total: ☐ p

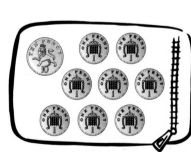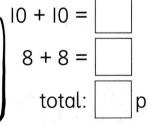

10 + 10 = ☐

8 + 8 = ☐

total: ☐ p

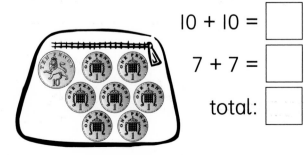

10 + 10 = ☐

7 + 7 = ☐

total: ☐ p

10 + 10 = ☐

q + q = ☐

total: ☐ p

Double

| Double the number of cubes. | 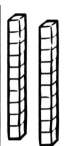 | 20 + 20 = ☐ |

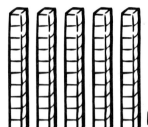 60 + 60 = ☐   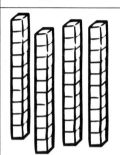 40 + 40 = ☐

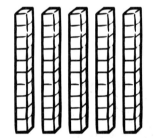 50 + 50 = ☐   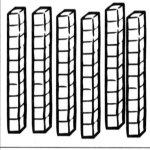 90 + 90 = ☐

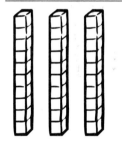 30 + 30 = ☐   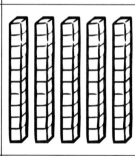 80 + 80 = ☐

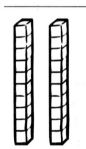
20 + 20 = ☐
3 + 3 = ☐
total: ☐

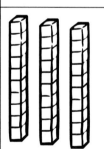
30 + 30 = ☐
2 + 2 = ☐
total: ☐

40 + 40 = ☐
1 + 1 = ☐
total: ☐

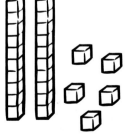
20 + 20 = ☐
5 + 5 = ☐
total: ☐

Name —————————————————

Doubling

Write how much
2 of each cost.

25p + 25p = ☐ p

15p + 15p = ☐ p

45p + 45p = ☐ p

35p + 35p = ☐ p

65p + 65p = ☐ p

55p + 55p = ☐ p

95p + 95p = ☐ p

5p + 5p = ☐ p

75p + 75p = ☐ p

Doubling

Double each
number.

24

$20 + 20 =$ ☐

$4 + 4 =$ ☐

total: ☐

41

☐ + ☐ = ☐

☐ + ☐ = ☐

total: ☐

33

☐ + ☐ = ☐

☐ + ☐ = ☐

total: ☐

22

☐ + ☐ = ☐

☐ + ☐ = ☐

total: ☐

44

☐ + ☐ = ☐

☐ + ☐ = ☐

total: ☐

15

☐ + ☐ = ☐

☐ + ☐ = ☐

total: ☐

14

☐ + ☐ = ☐

☐ + ☐ = ☐

total: ☐

26

☐ + ☐ = ☐

☐ + ☐ = ☐

total: ☐

32

☐ + ☐ = ☐

☐ + ☐ = ☐

total: ☐

38

☐ + ☐ = ☐

☐ + ☐ = ☐

total: ☐

Continue doubling.

2　4

Name ————————————————

Halves

Draw a line to divide each shape in half.

Colour each half differently.

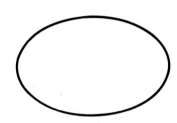 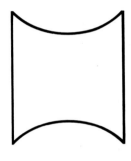 

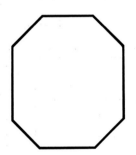 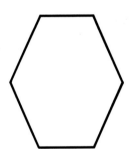 

Draw your own shape. Colour each half differently.

Quarters

Draw two lines to divide each shape in quarters.

Colour each quarter differently.

 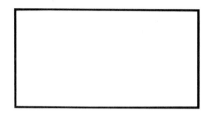 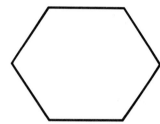

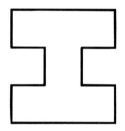  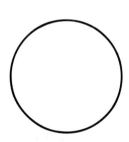

 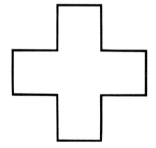 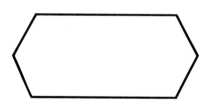

Draw your own shape. Colour each quarter differently.

Name _____

Halves and quarters

Colour one half and one quarter of these strips.

Build your own strips to help you.

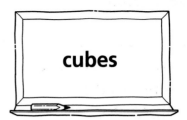

cubes

4	cubes

$\dfrac{1}{2}$ ⟶ ☐

$\dfrac{1}{4}$ ⟶ ☐

☐ cubes

$\dfrac{1}{2}$ ⟶ ☐

$\dfrac{1}{4}$ ⟶ ☐

☐ cubes

$\dfrac{1}{2}$ ⟶ ☐

$\dfrac{1}{4}$ ⟶ ☐

☐ cubes

$\dfrac{1}{2}$ ⟶ ☐

$\dfrac{1}{4}$ ⟶ ☐

☐ cubes

$\dfrac{1}{2}$ ⟶ ☐

$\dfrac{1}{4}$ ⟶ ☐

☐ cubes

$\dfrac{1}{2}$ ⟶ ☐

$\dfrac{1}{4}$ ⟶ ☐

Name

Three quarters

Colour three quarters of the sweets in each set.

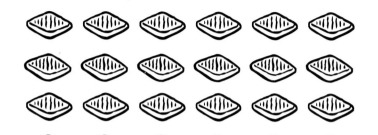

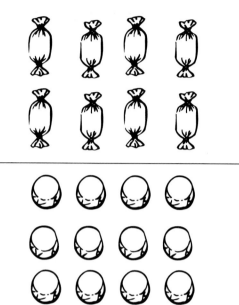

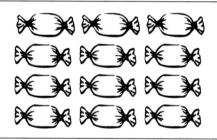

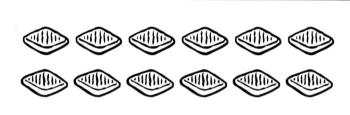

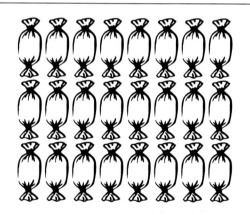

Rounding

```
├──┼──┼──┼──┼──┼──┼──┼──┼──┼──┼──┼──┼──┼──┼──┼──┼──┼──┼──┼──┼──┼──┼──┤
0   1   2   3   4   5   6   7   8   9  10  11  12  13  14  15  16  17  18  19  20  21  22  23
```

Write if these numbers are nearest to 0, 10 or 20.

7 ⟶ | 10 |

17 ⟶ ☐	8 ⟶ ☐	12 ⟶ ☐
19 ⟶ ☐	4 ⟶ ☐	21 ⟶ ☐
9 ⟶ ☐	18 ⟶ ☐	16 ⟶ ☐
13 ⟶ ☐	2 ⟶ ☐	11 ⟶ ☐
14 ⟶ ☐	22 ⟶ ☐	23 ⟶ ☐
1 ⟶ ☐	6 ⟶ ☐	3 ⟶ ☐

Rounding

Write the missing numbers

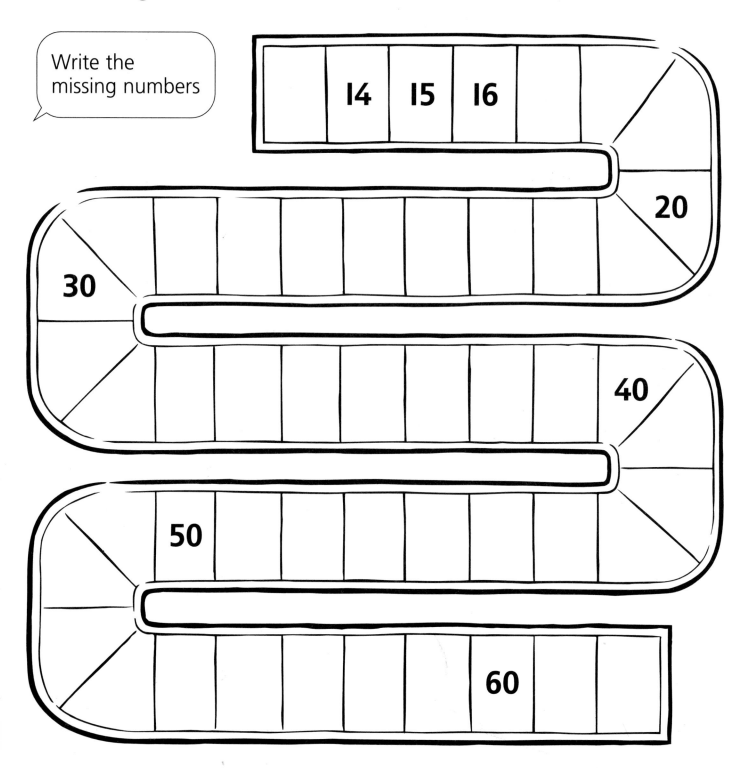

Colour the numbers: red if they are nearest 20
blue if they are nearest 30
yellow if they are nearest 40
pink if they are nearest 50
orange if they are nearest 60.

Rounding

Write the nearest ten for each number.

Use a number line, 1 to 50, to help you.

47 → 50	28 → ☐	32 → ☐
39 → ☐	41 → ☐	33 → ☐
19 → ☐	12 → ☐	24 → ☐
26 → ☐	36 → ☐	48 → ☐
46 → ☐	42 → ☐	31 → ☐
49 → ☐	45 → ☐	37 → ☐
23 → ☐	17 → ☐	11 → ☐
38 → ☐	29 → ☐	43 → ☐

47

Name —————————————————————

Rounding

How many 10p coins do you need to buy each item?

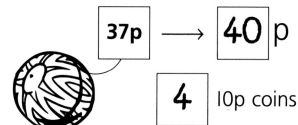

37p ⟶ **40** p

4 10p coins

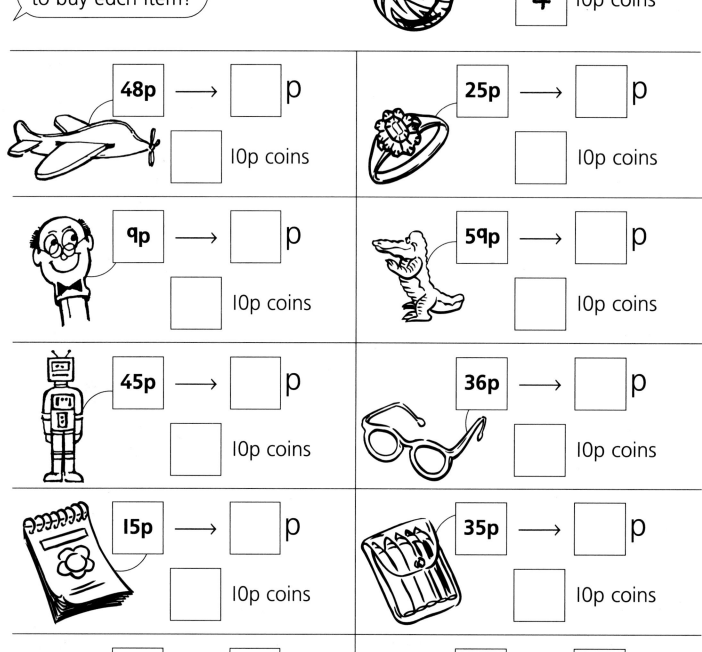

48p ⟶ ☐ p

☐ 10p coins

25p ⟶ ☐ p

☐ 10p coins

9p ⟶ ☐ p

☐ 10p coins

59p ⟶ ☐ p

☐ 10p coins

45p ⟶ ☐ p

☐ 10p coins

36p ⟶ ☐ p

☐ 10p coins

15p ⟶ ☐ p

☐ 10p coins

35p ⟶ ☐ p

☐ 10p coins

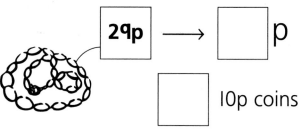

29p ⟶ ☐ p

☐ 10p coins

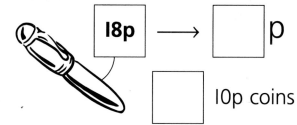

18p ⟶ ☐ p

☐ 10p coins

Name ———————————————————

Adding

Add each pair
and write the total.

30 40

total: 70

50 20

total: [ ]

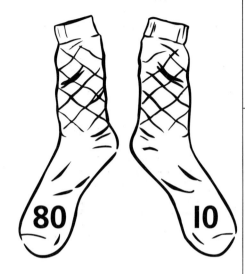

80 10

total: [ ]

50 30

total: [ ]

60 20

total: [ ]

70 20

total: [ ]

50 40

total: [ ]

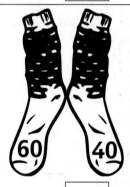

60 40

total: [ ]

Complete this
addition table.

+	20	30	40	50	60	70	80	90
20								
30								

Name _____

Estimate how much

> Round the first number to its nearest ten.

> Add the second number.

39 + 20
↓
40 + 20 = 60

27 + 30
↓
☐ + 30 = ☐

42 + 30
↓
☐ + 30 = ☐

52 + 20
↓
☐ + 20 = ☐

49 + 40
↓
☐ + 40 = ☐

61 + 20
↓
☐ + 20 = ☐

46 + 30
↓
☐ + 30 = ☐

72 + 20
↓
☐ + 20 = ☐

68 + 30
↓
☐ + 30 = ☐

34 + 40
↓
☐ + 40 = ☐

Name _____

Estimate how much

Round each price to its nearest ten. — Add 30p.

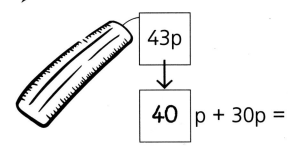

43p → 40 p + 30p = 70 p

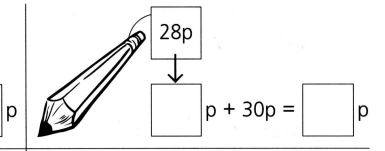

28p → ☐ p + 30p = ☐ p

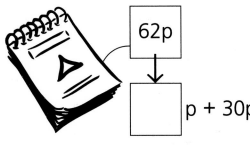

62p → ☐ p + 30p = ☐ p

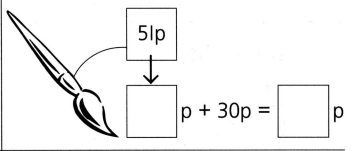

51p → ☐ p + 30p = ☐ p

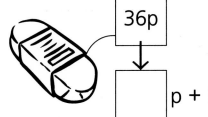

36p → ☐ p + 30p = ☐ p

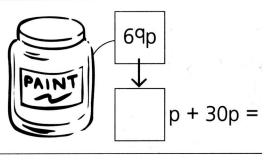

69p → ☐ p + 30p = ☐ p

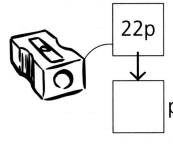

22p → ☐ p + 30p = ☐ p

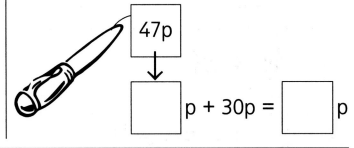

47p → ☐ p + 30p = ☐ p

Complete this table.

Round first, then add.

	36	49	21	64	79	33	59	44
nearest ten	40							
+	20	20	30	10	20	50	30	40
total	60							

Estimate how much.

Round each number to its nearest ten. ‒ Complete the additions.

64 + 22
↓   ↓
$60 + 20 = 80$

53 + 36
↓   ↓
☐ + ☐ = ☐

48 + 24
↓   ↓
☐ + ☐ = ☐

44 + 29
↓   ↓
☐ + ☐ = ☐

36 + 32
↓   ↓
☐ + ☐ = ☐

61 + 28
↓   ↓
☐ + ☐ = ☐

71 + 18
↓   ↓
☐ + ☐ = ☐

59 + 18
↓   ↓
☐ + ☐ = ☐

66 + 17
↓   ↓
☐ + ☐ = ☐

76 + 11
↓   ↓
☐ + ☐ = ☐

Counting on

Complete these. Use the tracks to help you.

$13 - 5 = \boxed{8}$

Point at 5

Count on, drawing a spot in each space.

Stop at 13. How many spots?

$12 - 8 = \square$

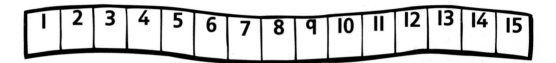

$15 - 7 = \square$

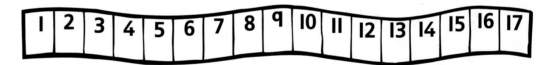

$18 - 9 = \square$

$17 - 8 = \square$

$16 - 10 = \square$

Counting on

| 1 | 2 | 3 | 4 | 5 | 6 | 7 | 8 | 9 | 10 | 11 | 12 | 13 | 14 | 15 | 16 | 17 | 18 | 19 | 20 |

Complete these. Use the track to help you.

$15 - 6 = \boxed{}$ $12 - 8 = \boxed{}$ $17 - 9 = \boxed{}$

$14 - 10 = \boxed{}$ $18 - 6 = \boxed{}$ $13 - 11 = \boxed{}$

$20 - 13 = \boxed{}$ $19 - 9 = \boxed{}$ $12 - 3 = \boxed{}$

$17 - 4 = \boxed{}$ $15 - 8 = \boxed{}$ $13 - 7 = \boxed{}$

$14 - 6 = \boxed{}$ $10 - 5 = \boxed{}$ $20 - 10 = \boxed{}$

$13 - 5 = \boxed{}$ $14 - 7 = \boxed{}$ $15 - 7 = \boxed{}$

Name ____________________

Counting on

Colour each card and its matching answer.

Use one colour for each pair.

16 – 4

5

13 – 9

18 – 15

4

17 – 9

12

9

11 – 1

11

20 – 9

16 – 11

3

8

6

17 – 8

10 – 4

16 – 9

7

10

Counting on

> Write how much more Joe has than each of his friends.

 **19p**

 **Joe**

 **13p**  **Sally**

| 19 |p – | 13 |p = | 6 |p

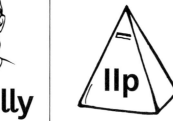 **11p** **Fred**

☐ p – ☐ p = ☐ p

 **9p**   **Lee**

☐ p – ☐ p = ☐ p

 **12p**  **Dave**

☐ p – ☐ p = ☐ p

 **15p**  **Seema**

☐ p – ☐ p = ☐ p

 **8p**  **Jade**

☐ p – ☐ p = ☐ p

 **2p**  **Anup**

☐ p – ☐ p = ☐ p

 **7p** **Ann**

☐ p – ☐ p = ☐ p

 **10p**  **John**

☐ p – ☐ p = ☐ p

Name ————————————

Fives

Write the missing
numbers on each track.

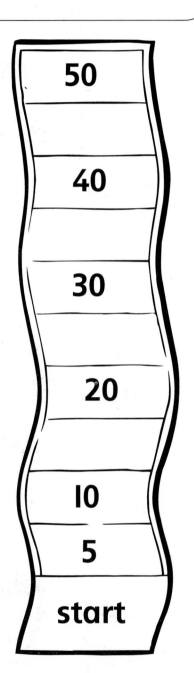

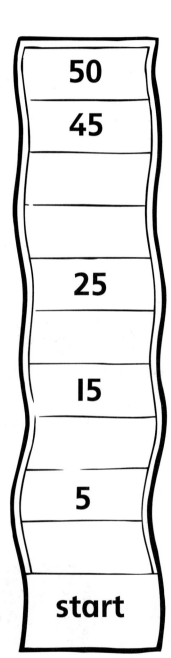

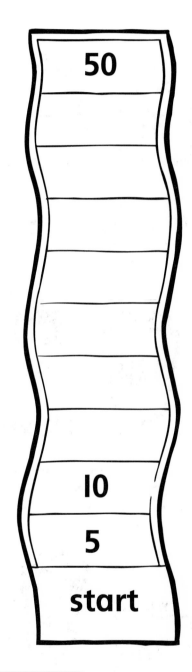

Place one counter
on each 'start'.

Throw a dice
and move each
counter in turn.

Which counter
reaches the
end first?

Fives

Draw a line between each ball and the matching boot.

Use 5p coins to help you.

5×5

10×5

5

8×5

2 $\times$ 5
(ball)

25

20

9×5

10

7×5

35

1×5

50

4×5

15

45

3×5

40

6×5

30

Name _____

Fives

Cover each number with 5p coins to match.

Place one 5p coin on 5, two 5p coins on 10, and so on.

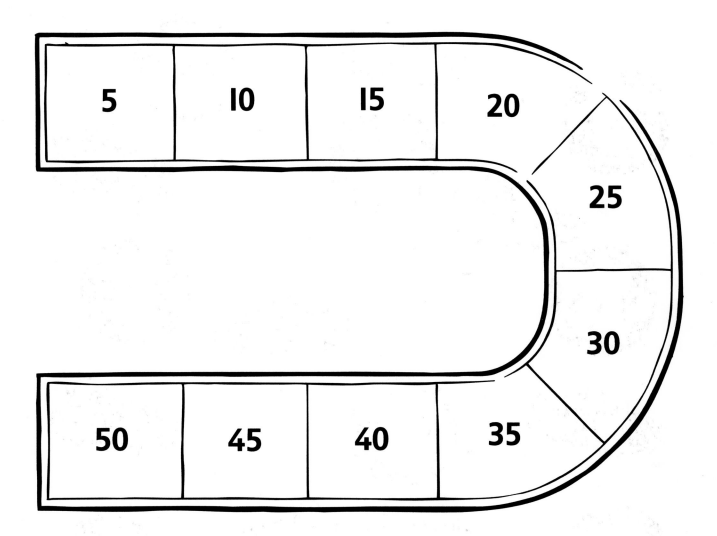

5 10 15 20 25 30 35 40 45 50

Choose a pile of coins and guess which number is underneath.

Check to see if you are correct.

Fives

Write the missing numbers.

☐ × 5 = 20   2 × 5 = ☐

☐ × 5 = 15   1 × 5 = ☐

☐ × 5 = 25   6 × 5 = ☐

☐ × 5 = 35   8 × 5 = ☐

☐ × 5 = 5   9 × 5 = ☐

☐ × 5 = 50   7 × 5 = ☐

Each finger stands for 5.   Write how many fives and the answer.

3 × 5 = 15

☐ × 5 = ☐

☐ × 5 = ☐

☐ × 5 = ☐

☐ × 5 = ☐

☐ × 5 = ☐

Rows

Write how
many buns.

$2 \times 4 =$ **8**

$2 \times 5 =$ ☐

$3 \times 6 =$ ☐

$4 \times 7 =$ ☐

$2 \times 9 =$ ☐

$3 \times 8 =$ ☐

$4 \times 4 =$ ☐

$4 \times 5 =$ ☐

Name ——————————————————

Rows

Write the missing numbers.

Complete the rows of buns to help you.

$3 \times \boxed{3} = 9$

$2 \times \boxed{} = 12$

$4 \times \boxed{} = 16$

$5 \times \boxed{} = 15$

$2 \times \boxed{} = 10$

$3 \times \boxed{} = 18$

$2 \times \boxed{} = 14$

$4 \times \boxed{} = 20$

Name _____

Rows

Write the missing numbers. Draw rows of buns to help you.

 2 rows, 16 buns in total

3 rows, 18 buns in total

$2 \times \boxed{} = 16$

$3 \times \boxed{} = 18$

$2 \times \boxed{} = 18$

$4 \times \boxed{} = 24$

$5 \times \boxed{} = 20$

$2 \times \boxed{} = 20$

$3 \times \boxed{} = 21$

$3 \times \boxed{} = 12$

Name _____

Division

Share each amount equally between 4 children.

Use real coins to help you.

$8p \div 4 = \boxed{} \, p$

$16p \div 4 = \boxed{} \, p$

$20p \div 4 = \boxed{} \, p$

$12p \div 4 = \boxed{} \, p$

$4p \div 4 = \boxed{} \, p$

$24p \div 4 = \boxed{} \, p$

Complete these divisions.

Draw rows of crosses to help you.

X X X X X
X X X X X

$10 \div 5 = \boxed{}$

$14 \div 7 = \boxed{}$

$27 \div 9 = \boxed{}$

$21 \div 7 = \boxed{}$